Table of Contents:

MW00892367

Introduction:

Dear reader: Thanks for downloading this book. A few months ago, a T.V. program caught my attention. The newscaster was talking about the amazing health benefits of this "secret tea". Out of curiosity, I searched for Matcha tea on the Internet. It turned out that this "secret tea" is very old. My next task was to search out all the information I could about Matcha tea. It took me months to research the content in this book. I have been a regular Matcha tea drinker since the last five months, and it feels great. I will not keep you waiting. Let's get started.

Chapter 1: What is Matcha green tea?

The beautiful art of Matcha tea has made its way into the United States and around the world. The drink is favorably compared to a great cup of Starbucks coffee or other caffeinated beverages. Matcha literally means "powdered tea." Matcha has a unique vegetal, bitter, malty taste. Many have said it tastes like seaweed with its foaming texture and vibrant color based on green tea leaves. When you order traditional tea, the leaves get infused into hot water and the leaves are then discarded. With Matcha, you're drinking the actual leaves, which have been finely ground and made into a powder. You mix about a teaspoon of Matcha powder with a third cup of hot water (hot - not boiled), which is then whisked with a bamboo brush until it froths. Yum!

Benefits?

Matcha tea has gained extreme popularity because of its health benefits. It doesn't raise blood pressure or your heart rate, making it a safe alternative to many drugs that are full of side effects. And what else? Matcha tea makes you relaxed, alert but calm. Since you are consuming whole leaves in Matcha so you may get three times as much caffeine than a cup of steeped tea, about the amount in a cup of brewed coffee. Matcha lovers say that compared to the caffeine buzz from coffee, Matcha creates an "alert calm" due to a natural substance it contains called L-Theanine, which induces relaxation without drowsiness. Matcha does not put any stress on the body. No side effects are attached with the Matcha tea.

Weight Loss?

Green tea has caffeine that contains specific antioxidants that can help with your metabolism rate and weight loss. Matcha can be a great addition to a weight loss program as it boosts metabolism and burns fat. One study suggested that Matcha might speed up the burning of calories by four times. A study featured in the American Journal of Clinical Nutrition found that consuming Matcha could increase thermo genesis (the body's rate of burning calories) from a normal 8%-10% of daily energy expenditure, to between 35% and 43% of daily energy expenditure.

How Do You Drink it?

It is traditionally enjoyed in a Matcha bowl without any additives. To appeal to the American palate many cafés add sugar to Matcha powder and steamed milk to make the trendy Matcha latte. (Keep reading and you will find a Matcha latte recipe at the end of this book.)

On social media people ask two questions:

1. What is that Matcha drink?

2. Why is it getting popular?

How is Matcha green tea different from the old green tea? Matcha is a fine ground powder gained from the processed green tea. All types of green tea are extracted from the same plant. In case of Matcha green tea, we consume full leaves without discarding nutritional parts. The fine green tea powder is extracted in a two-part procedure i.e., farming and processing. In the farming process, the plant leaves are shade grown for almost 21 days. Stem and veins are removed in the processing part. Matcha tea has concentrated green tea elements that are famous for their anti-cancer properties and other health benefits.

When the Matcha leaves are exposed to direct sunlight, the production of L-Theanine is rapidly increased. L-Theanine has proven health benefits that will be discussed in a later chapter. The processing of the Matcha leaves is accomplished in a very specific way. As mentioned earlier, Matcha leaves are exposed to sunlight before harvesting. This produces further two types of leaves i.e., those that are naturally rolled and the ones that are dried. The difference in texture produces two different tea types. The rolled leaves produce the "Gyokoro", and the dried leaves are used to prepare the Matcha green tea.

Wise men chose Matcha because of health benefits it offers. The research suggests that 1 cup of Matcha tea offers the nutritional value of 10 cups of regular green tea. If you need 270 mg of EGCG per day for losing weight, you will need to drink 7-10 cups of green tea. Compared to regular tea, you will only need to drink one cup of Matcha.

Matcha Vs. Regular Green Tea

According to the 2003 study by the University of Colorado, powdered Matcha has 137 times more anti-oxidants as compared to the regular green tea.

What is regular green tea? In many studies, Matcha tea is compared to the lowest quality green tea sold in America. In such a comparison, Matcha tea always wins. Japan is the best manufacturer of the highest quality tea products. In Japan, when you compare Matcha to other green tea leaves, you will notice following figures:

- High-quality green tea: Number of anti-oxidants: 100 milligrams per 1 gram
- Powdered green tea: Number of anti-oxidants: 119 milligrams per 1 gram
- Matcha green tea: Number of anti-oxidants: 127 milligrams per 1 gram

Green tea contains very important nutritional elements such as the ECGC, catechin, theanine, caffeine and L-Theanine. The EGCG acts as an anti-cancer guide for your body. When you consume, Matcha, the dose of EGCG becomes 10% higher, and it may significantly reduce your chances to attract cancer.

With simple green tea intake, you increase your metabolism rate by 8%. By drinking Matcha tea, the metabolism rate can be increased to 25%.

Caffeine in Green Tea Vs. Matcha Vs. Coffee

Caffeine is an important nutritional element in coffee and green tea. It stimulates the nervous system while making you more alert and active. In America, some people drink coffee to receive an energy boost to concentrate on their work. It is a good idea in the beginning, but ultimately it destroys the natural equilibrium. An overdose of caffeine may result in dizziness, vomiting, insomnia, diarrhea, and the disturbed respiratory system. Caffeinated drinks are not recommended for some athletes.

The amazing health benefits of tea have motivated Americans to drink tea in the Chinese way. Matcha tea has been brought to Americans by the Japanese tradition. Green tea contains significantly less amount of caffeine as compared to coffee. The nutritional info of green tea and the Matcha is highly affected by temperature.

You will miss an amazing portion of nutrients if you pour boiling water in the green tea mixture. It is also noticed that drinking green tea after 10 minutes, reduces the caffeine intake by 50% i.e., 32 mg of caffeine value drops to 12 mg. It is good news for people who want the benefits of green tea without consuming extra caffeine. A comparison of caffeine content is showed below:

50 mg/100 ml - Coffee
32 gm/100ml – Green Tea
20mg/100 ml – Energy Drink
8.75mg/100ml – Matcha Tea

Matcha Vs. Coffee

Americans love coffee. In fact, coffee is appreciated in the entire world. This aromatic drink tastes good and is now flavored in different ways. One of the most famous coffee brands is Starbucks. Starbucks is the largest coffee business brand with more than 21,536 stores located worldwide at this current date.

The question is can we compare Matcha tea with our favorite Starbucks drink? Matcha tea recently found its way from Japan to America. People are enthusiastic about this grassy drink. Matcha tea is becoming more of a style item than a pure health drink. Obviously, it has amazing health benefits, and it does not matter whether you drink it in one specific style or another one. Many Matcha tea recipes have been created, and I assume that famous brand names will start offering Matcha tea on their menus.

In this section, we'll discuss the nutritional value of Matcha tea when compared to coffee.

Reasons to drink Matcha instead of Coffee

1. You consume coffee to receive a boost of energy with some good taste. Matcha is not advertised as the energy drink, but the good nutritional value provides enough energy for a calm day.

2. Matcha has a low amount of Caffeine. Matcha contains flavonoids that keep you fresh for a long time. Compare this to coffee, which gives you a burst of energy with 50 mg of caffeine per 100 ml.

3. Matcha is a natural drink. The popularity of Matcha suggests that people are looking a healthy change. After all, coffee or energy drinks cannot replace pure natural drinks.

4. You may be able to drink Matcha during pregnancy when all other highly caffeinated drinks are not recommended.

The caffeine content in star bucks drinks can be found in this article: http://www.caffeineinformer.com/the-complete-guide-to-starbucks-caffeine

Matcha Vs. Sencha

What is the difference between Matcha and Sencha? In this section, we'll discover the differences between these two green tea types. Green tea, Matcha, and Sencha are all derived from the same tree named Camellia Sinensis.

The basic difference is created during the farming process. Matcha leaves are shaded for 21-30 days before harvesting. Sencha leaves grow in open air and sunlight. The exposure to sunlight reduces the number of amino acids in Sencha. On the contrary, Matcha contains more amino acids.

Another difference is the physical structure. Because of the shading, Matcha leaves are flat, and their ground powder has a very fine and smooth texture. Matcha leaves are bright green. Compared to Matcha, Sencha leaves have a dark green color. Matcha drink has a creamy flavor while Sencha offers a refreshing taste.

Both tea types allow you to consume whole tea leaf, and thus both Sencha & Matcha leaves are healthier for consumption than any other tea or coffee.

Sencha contains more antioxidants than Matcha. It probably happens because of the sun exposure. On the other hand, Matcha is the powerhouse of L-Theanine and offers more relaxation.

It's hard to recommend one tea type over the other. Sencha is one of the best tea leaves produced. On the other hand, Matcha tea is a becoming a new fashion and an emerging health trend. It has less amount of caffeine and it provides consistent energy for day-to-day tasks.

Matcha Tea Powder (Notice the fine texture of the Matcha tea.)

Sencha Tea Powder

Matcha Vs. Gyokuro

Matcha is very similar to Gyokuro. Unlike Sencha, Gyokuro leaves are shaded a month before the harvesting season. This act saves many amino acids, reduces the bitterness in flavor and results in bright green flat leaves. You can think of Matcha as the powdered form of Gyokuro leaves. What makes Matcha special is the Japanese tea ceremony. Matcha tea is specifically made for the tea ceremony. In Japan, most commonly Sencha tea is used. You will find Sencha tea at different prices in different qualities. The difference between Matcha and the Gyokuro is their cooking process. To prepare Gyokuro, you pour boiling water on the leaves. To prepare Matcha tea, you must not use hot (boiling water). Set it aside for 5 minutes and then, you can prepare the tea. Also, you must use a whisk to form the creamy texture of the Matcha drink.

Gyokuro leaves are rolled and dried. Matcha leaves are not rolled. These leaves are dried and then steamed. In China, tea leaves are also fried. However in Japan, steaming the Tenhca leaves produces Matcha tea. The "Tenhca" defines the rolled and dried Gyokuro leaves.

There are other green tea types that can be compared to Matcha tea, i.e. Genmaicha, Hojicha, Shincha, and Ryo Kucha. I have discussed the most popular tea types, and that brings us to the end of our first chapter.

So, what is Matcha?

In the dictionary, Matcha means, "powdered tea". However, in the traditional world, Matcha refers to a specific ground powder gained from the green tea leaves. Let's move forward because a beautiful traditional ceremony is waiting for you.

Chapter 2: Matcha tea – Why so Popular?

The Japanese made Matcha a way of their life. Not only, they did celebrate the tea ceremony, but they practiced the philosophy behind the Matcha tea. It promotes a certain state of mind that is most likely to be accomplished by meditation.

Matcha tea relaxes the nervous system, improves focus, and builds stability in your life. It was not until the 20th century that Matcha tea was introduced in the European countries. Americans still drink three times more coffee as compared to tea. However, the tea industry has seen growth in sales for more than 10 billion dollars. Increased popularity of Matcha will surely change these statistics in a positive way as people are introduced to the amazing benefits of Matcha tea.

The Internet has made it possible to know the Japanese culture in an easy way. You can recognize why the Japanese started the ceremony hundreds of years ago. It is time to introduce Matcha tea in your life.

Most people prefer Matcha to the coffee drink because of the effect on nervous system. Drinking coffee may have negative effects on your heart. Also, the caffeine in Matcha is fairly different than the caffeine present in regular tea and coffee. The caffeine in Matcha provides consistent energy while the caffeine in other items seem to increase your heart beat rate and disturbs the biological rhythm.

Why is Matcha tea is becoming popular in America?

In recent years, Americans have shifted their eating habits. Preference is leaning towards more natural food as compared to the commercially produced foods. Matcha tea is a step ahead in our journey of natural eating.

All the health related blogs and celebrities are talking about Matcha tea. Starbucks has also played a major role to increase the popularity. The inclusion of green tea on the Starbucks menu, markets the drink to a greater audience.

Tea companies are planning to offer a more westernized version of Matcha. Sometimes, sweeteners are added to reduce the bitterness of the Matcha tea. Matcha has a very strong taste. Some people may refer it to a seaweed, grassy flavor or spinach flavored.

Health benefits of the Matcha tea

The regular consumption of Matcha drink brings many benefits for your health. I am going to present a short list. It is important to note that Matcha tea has more antioxidants than any other tea. Also, you are consuming the whole leaf. It means you
are consuming a high amount of lead and soluble fibers. Drinking Matcha tea is a good idea, but Matcha Madness can be harmful to your health. Please limit your daily Matcha intake to 1-2 cups maximum. Health benefits are listed below:

- The high number of antioxidants works amazingly well for your skin.

- Matcha tea has the EGCG elements. These elements are known for their anti-cancer properties. It also has been said to help with diabetes, arthritis, heart disease, liver disease, and the chronic fatigue syndrome.

- L-Theanine is used to improve memory and stimulates the nervous system. Experts also noticed an increase in the alpha activity.

- Matcha tea leaves are shaded for about a month. This step increases the amount of chlorophyll resulting in vibrant green tea leaves. The strong presence of chlorophyll makes Matcha tea a very detoxifying drink. It removes toxins and is said to help with weight loss.

- Matcha tea is the host of vitamin A, vitamin C, potassium, magnesium, calcium, protein, and iron. These ingredients make Matcha tea a responsible factor to improve the body's immune system.

- Matcha green tea has a very refreshing and grassy flavor.

- A very healthy and organic drink without artificial additives.

Chapter 3: The History of Matcha Tea

We all know that the tea plant was brought from China to Japan. The historical records suggest that the first tea plant was grown in the Yunnan province in Southern China. The production then progressed to some cities in Asia. The tea plant was reserved for the royal members.

The introduction of tea to the general population happened in 2700 B.C. in the state of Emperor Shen Nong. Then, appeared the bible of tea making, the original book, "Cha Jing". The book is referred to as the book of tea. Author Lu Yu wrote the book in 760 A.D.

The 8th century saw the commercial opening of teashops in many cities. It is suggested that the Matcha tea plant was introduced in Japan in 794-1185 A.D. According to another source, Zen Monk Eisai brought the tea plant to Japan in 1191 A.D.

Eisai introduced Zen philosophy to the Japanese audience. He was the first person who prepared tea from these green leaves. Very soon, Zen and the Matcha became synonym with each other. In 1215 A.D., Matcha tea was introduced to the general population and soon this opening gave birth to the famous Japanese tea ceremony. The tea ceremony was the first ritual to display the oneness of the Matcha drink and the Zen art.

Chapter 4: The Japanese Tea Ceremony

Simplicity should be entertained in every walk of life. Trying to achieve happiness by accomplishing more and more often does not work. We all need to stop and focus. There is no better way to explain the benefits of Matcha tea than explaining this ceremony. This ceremony is celebrated in a specific manner many times in a year.

The 4th century introduced the benefits of tea to the Chinese audience. Japanese did not have tea seeds until the relationship between these two countries was nurtured. Most surveys suggest that the ceremony was started in the 9th century.

Influence of the book, "Cha Jing."

Published in the 18th century, this book explains the basics of tea making, beverage drinking, right proportion, the cooking method, and the benefits of tea drinking. It is believed that this book shaped the future of tea drinking in Japan.

Another famous book is "The Classics of Tea: Origin & Rituals". The original information is also available in English. While some great books were published in the 8th century, very limited information is available in English. In the 8th century, tea extracts were mostly available in the medicine or for meditation. The 9th century revealed the amazing spiritual & health benefits of drinking tea. (Today, the tea is known as Matcha.)

Some of the other classical books are listed below:

"Chado, the Way of Tea" by Sasaki Sanmi

"The Japanese Tea Ceremony" by Seno Tanaka

"The Book of Tea" by Kakuzo Okakura

"Matcha Green Tea, a Beginner's Guide" is an attempt to take this information to the next level.

The philosophy & the procedure of the tea ceremony

Tea is different from all other beverages and caffeine based drinks. We drink coffee for the benefits of caffeine. We drink tea to be more relaxed, consciously alert and to be awake to new possibilities. You might have never realized the true benefits of drinking tea. It is an ordinary drink for many because the philosophy has been ignored. In Japan tea became a subject for poetry in the 19th century. It was a sacred drink for amusement that was said to contain healing powers as it was introduced in the medicines. The tea trees were respected just like the sun and the stars.

Japan is a country where art is displayed in a very humble and beautiful manner. According to the book, "The Way of Tea":

> "There are three schools to teach the philosophy of tea drinking. Our greatness lies in expressing ourselves. Since life is a beautiful expression of the higher self, it is our job to express ourselves harmoniously and piously. The true expression is the art of happiness. The aromatic sips of green tea are refreshing enough to make you alert to new opportunities. It is the best beverage to start your day. "

The tea schools are categorized in three sections i.e., the Classic, the Romantic, and the Naturalistic schools of Tea. The evolution of tea progressed in three stages: the boiled tea, the whipped tea, and the steeped tea. Centuries have seen the development of tea in China and Japan. The Japanese tea ceremony is a further step to teach the art of tea making.

The point of the Japanese tea making ceremony is to keep it simple and beautiful. You can celebrate this event at your home, or in a special tearoom. Specific gestures are practiced to make the event perfect.

The procedure of this ceremony is simple:

As a guest in a tea room, you will have to wait in a room before the tea is ready. Then, you can walk your way to a basin to wash your hands. Slowly, you will enter the room as your host will be waiting for you. You will bow to greet the host and he/she will do the same. Modern times have changed the ceremony. Initially, the ceremony was restricted to the tea drinks only. Now, you may be served, Wagashi and Chai. These words mean, "sweets" and "a complete meal" respectively. After treating yourself with these delicious food items, the tea will be presented.

Specific utensils are used to prepare Japanese green tea.

www.matchaandmore.com

This image perfectly explains the required utensils that you will be using in your home. It is a bamboo whisk with a bamboo scoop. The big one is the tea bowl also known as the Chawan in Japanese. A specific kettle is used to prepare the tea. It is a traditional utensil. In most recipes, we will not use the "kama".

The green tea caddy contains the concentrated tea. The mixing bowl is called the "Kensui." We'll simply call it the bowl with a wooden spoon.

People in the west, practice the art of this Japanese tea ceremony. Here are a few steps to achieve that spirit:

1. Close your eyes and purify your heart of all thoughts. Focus on the tea making process only.

2. Wash your hands carefully.

3. Wash all the utensils for tea making.

4. In the tradition, all people drink from the same bowl. You can buy different bowls for your family.

These Japanese traditions are taught in every school in Japan. Students learn the discipline of the Japanese tea ceremony as well as the duties of the host. Colleges teach students the etiquette to enter the tearoom, how to make tea properly, how to serve the guests, and how to observe the spirit of this ceremony.

Chapter 5: How to Buy Quality Matcha Tea?

We have discussed the health benefits of Matcha tea. It is time to use Matcha tea. First, we will need to buy Matcha tea. The question is how do we buy the best organic green tea powder that is healthier and tastes good. It is important not to buy Matcha tea with added sweetness. It is also important to know the production process of each tea type. The difference in production gives birth to the specific properties of each tea type. In China, the tea leaves are dried and then fried thoroughly. To prepare Matcha drink, we do not need fried leaves. Experts prefer steamed leaves in the Japanese way. The brand name and the price are also a factor while purchasing the Matcha tea.

Local coffee shops offer green tea drinks. You may find the Matcha tea at some local shops. As popularity grows you may find Matcha tea offered more and more in your town. You can also prepare Matcha at your home. For this purpose, you will need to buy Matcha tea that mostly comes in canned tins. It will come along with a nutritional info chart, and a recipe manual.

Matcha tea powder is used in many other sweets and ice creams. In the last chapter, I will share some Matcha tea recipes.

Here are some tips in buying Matcha:

1. Check the color. Since all green tea types are extracted from the same plant, it is important to notice the texture, smell, and color of the green tea. The color of Matcha should be grassy green because of the presence of chlorophyll.

2. Check the consistency. Matcha tea is a very fine powder. If the tealeaves are not in a very fine ground powder, you should not buy it.

3. The taste of Matcha tea is not bitter. Sencha has a bitter taste, but Matcha should have a mild sweet taste.

4. Only buy Japanese Matcha.

5. Only buy the organic Matcha. Avoid artificial additives to enjoy a fresh enhancing grassy smell.

6. Buy steamed Matcha leaves. Fried leaves are not good for your health.

High-Quality Vs. Low-Quality Matcha

I am sharing two pictures from the website: www.thedailytea.com. Check out these pictures to understand the difference between high quality and low-quality Matcha tea.

Low-quality Matcha before whisk

High-quality Matcha before whisk

Low-quality Matcha after whisk

High-quality Matcha after whisk

How to Order Matcha tea?

The increasing popularity of Matcha has made it possible to get the Matcha tea right at your doorstep. You can order Matcha tea from any website or a local shop. The important task is to choose the best brand with the best price. The price of Matcha tea is typically higher. Do not compromise quality for the price. Buying a cheap and low-quality Matcha tea will not help. High-quality Matcha offers a great flavor as well as amazing health benefits.

Matcha green tea is graded in 4 sectors. This information is presented for informational purpose only, and I am not promoting any specific brand.

1. **Ceremony Grade** - Name derived from the traditional tea ceremony

This grade is best for taste. It has a mild sweet taste. This tea is extracted from young and fresh leaves. Old leaves have a bitter taste whereas young leaves have a sweet taste.

2. **Classical Grade**- It offers a classical style

A great drink for health. This tea is extracted from the middle part of leaves.

3. **Cafe Grade**-It offers good quality with the cafe style

This type of tea is extracted from senior leaves. It is mostly used in desserts, ice creams, and smoothies.

4. **Kitchen Grade**- Offers good nutrition to be used with various dishes

Extracted from the corners of old leaves. It is used in green tea latte, smoothies, drinks, and different recipes.

I know you are excited to make the Matcha tea. Well! Our next chapter guides you to make the traditional Matcha. I have also included delicious Matcha recipes to surprise you! Let's move to the next chapter.

Chapter 6: How to prepare Matcha tea at home?

All you really need is a Matcha whisk, a measuring spoon and a bowl…but if you want to prepare it as they do in the East here are the full instructions for preparation.

Gather the instruments or the apparatus. Here is the list:

1. Measuring cup
2. Thermometer
3. Strainer
4. Teaspoon
5. Linen cloth piece
6. Organic Matcha
7. Bamboo whisk
8. Bamboo scoop
9. Matcha bowl
10. The kettle for heating the water

Open the bottle or the packet of the organic Matcha container. Take the Matcha bowl and pour some boiling water into it. This step is used to heat the bowl. Place the whisk prongs in the hot water to make it wet. After 2-3 minutes, empty the bowl. Clean and dry the bowl with the linen cloth piece. Now measure water in the cup. You should decide the thickness & thinness of the tea. If you want a thick drink, add 2 2/4 Tablespoons (40 ml) of water for one dose, add more to thin it out.

Now measure three scoops of Matcha powder if you want a lighter taste. Add five scoops of Matcha tea powder if you want a strong flavor. You can use the strainer to sift the Matcha powder. Measure the water temperature that should be 175 degrees Fahrenheit (80-degree Celsius). If you want to make a frothy liquid, whisk the bamboo in a "W" or "M" shape. If you want a thick liquid, whisk the bamboo in circular directions.

Whisk the liquid for 1-2 minutes. It should have a foamy texture and a bright green color. It should have tiny bubbles on the surface. You can pour the tea into a cup, but traditionally, it is preferred to drink it in the bowl. It has a very enhancing flavor that will keep you fresh all the daylong.

When you drink Matcha it is a sensory experience, here is how you should do it:

Cup the bowl with your hands, take it to your lips, and breathe in the Matcha aroma as you take a sip. The bowl acts as a sort of dome over your nose and mouth.

Matcha is new to the American industry. We have not figured the overdose of Matcha. It is best to enjoy 1 Matcha serving each day.

We have learned to make the traditional Matcha. Now, it is time to use Matcha tea in a different way to experience amazing new flavors.

Chapter 7: Matcha Recipes

Matcha Green Tea Latte Recipe

This recipe requires a frother, but we are going to use the bamboo whisk. If you have a frother, you can use it. Here are the ingredients:

1. Green tea Matcha powder (organic)
2. Hot water
3. Some hot milk

The cooking directions are the same as the traditional Matcha. Clean a Matcha bowl and add two teaspoons of the Matcha organic powder. Add 1 tbsp of hot water. Whisk the water to mix the Matcha powder in the water. Take your time and mix it carefully. Make a smooth paste. Take some sugar and water in the saucepan. Heat the milk. The temperature should be about 175 degrees Fahrenheit (80-degree Celsius). Pour the milk in the Matcha paste. Use the bamboo whisk or the frother to give a foamy texture. Whisk it about for one minute. The delicious Matcha green tea latte is ready!

Iced Matcha Green Tea Latte Recipe

It is pretty similar to the first recipe. You need one tsp of Matcha powder mixed it in 1 tbsp of hot water. You must *not* use boiling water. Have a cup of ice cubes ready. Add 2 tbsp of sugar syrup, 4 tbsp of milk, and one tsp of vanilla flavor. Add 4-6 ice cubes in a tall glass. Add the remaining ice in the blender with all the ingredients. Blend for a minute and pour in the glass.

Matcha Green Tea Latte Recipe from Starbucks

Add a half-cup of coconut milk or almond milk in a blender. Add one tsp of the Matcha tea powder. You can add 1-3 packets of Splenda or Stevia. It depends on your taste. Use a milk frother to prepare a creamy & foamy Starbucks drink.

Matcha Tea Smoothie – Here is a very simple recipe and great for breakfast too. Filled with vitamins, these smoothies are refreshing.

Use the cafe grade or the kitchen grade Matcha. Add ½ cup of plain yogurt in the electric blender. Add 2 tbsp honey or the sugar syrup. Add some ice cubes with one teaspoon of the Matcha powder. Blend the ingredients for a minute and serve in a fancy, tall glass.

Fruity Matcha Smoothie

This one contains fresh fruits. It is probably the freshest smoothie in this list. Add a full cup of strawberries, blueberries, blackberries, and raspberries. Add one teaspoon of Matcha with 1/2 cup of plain yogurt. You can also add sugar and some ice cubes. Blend for a minute. This smoothie has a beautiful color and a very refreshing taste.

Matcha Mango Smoothie

Take mango slices or 1 1/2 cups filled with mango chunks. Add 2 tbsp of honey or sugar syrup. Add 1/4 cup of plain yogurt with 1 cup of unsweetened milk in the blender. Add 1/2 or 1 tsp of Matcha tea powder. Blend the ingredients and serve it in a tall glass.

Mint-Matcha Smoothie

Take 3/4 cup of almond milk or any milk available at home. Add two large peeled bananas, 2 tbsp yogurt, some water, 1 tbsp sugar syrup, one tsp of Matcha tea powder and some mint leaves. Blend the ingredients for about 2 minutes. This smoothie has a wonderful green/yellowish color and a nice fragrance. You can use chopped almonds and shredded coconut for dressing.

Matcha Green Tea Ice-Cream

Here is a great way to consume Matcha. It is also good for kids. Here are the ingredients:

½ cup milk
Egg yolks from two eggs
6 tbsp of sugar
½ cup whipped heavy cream
2 Tbsp of hot water
1 Tbsp of Matcha powder

Whisk the Matcha tea in hot water in a separate bowl. Prepare the thick paste and put it aside. Whisk the egg yolks in a pan and add milk and sugar. Heat the pan over medium heat. Keep mixing to have consistent thickness. Remove the pan and put it in cold water. Set it aside and let it cool. Add the green tea powder in the egg combinations. Freeze it. Serve when it is frozen.

Conclusion

This brings us to the end of this book. I truly enjoyed writing this book. Many people start drinking Matcha because of the amazing health or weight loss benefits it offers. However, many will ignore the rich traditional background of this tea. Many say that the tea cannot bring its full benefits when you consume it in a cafe. Tradition tells us to focus on the tea making process and the tea itself. The whole tea should be consumed in 4-5 large sips. Feel that relaxed feeling traveling through your body. Notice the frothy texture and the grassy smell.

Some of you may not like Matcha because it tastes like grass or spinach. Many of you will adore the fragrance and the refreshing texture. To those who do not like the taste, you can add a bit of sugar. It is highly recommended that you drink the highest quality of Matcha tea. You should be using the ceremony grade. Also buy a frother. I have shared some recipes. Be creative, you can invent your own recipes. There are hundreds of ways to introduce Matcha in your daily life. Most of us are already consuming green tea. Drinking Matcha tea takes you a step further in the journey of health & fitness. Another good advantage is that you can replace that daily cup of coffee.

Matcha may not taste better than coffee, but it will help you get rid of those energy shocks, dizziness, and a faster heartbeat. Matcha tea makes you relaxed. No side effects are attached with the Matcha tea. My recommendation is that you do not consume more than 2 cups of Matcha tea. One cup of Matcha offers the nutritional value of 10 cups of regular green tea.

This book was aimed at beginners. Matcha is going to be one of the most celebrated drinks of the year. Get ahead of the trend and enjoy a healthy lifestyle.

If you find this book informative and helpful, please take your time to leave a review at Amazon.

Thanks!

Made in United States
Orlando, FL
20 December 2024

56196388R00021